THE GENIUS OF THOMAS "FATS" WALLER

Wise Publications
London / New York / Paris / Sydney / Copenhagen / Madrid

Exclusive Distributors:
Music Sales Limited
8/9 Frith Street, London W1V 5TZ, England.
Music Sales Pty Limited
120 Rothschild Avenue, Rosebery, NSW 2018, Australia.

Order No.AM939246
ISBN 0-7119-5981-1

Visit the Music Sales' Internet Music Shop at
http://www.musicsales.co.uk

Book design by Michael Bell Design.
Cover photograph courtesy of Redferns.

Printed in the United Kingdom by
Halstan & Co. Ltd., Amersham, Bucks.

Honeysuckle Rose

Words by Andy Razaf
Music by Thomas Waller

Dm7
G9
C
Cdim
C7
A♭dim
C7
A♭dim
sweet - er sweet - ness can't be found. You're so sweet, can't be
C7
D7-9
Gm
G9
Gm7
C9
beat, noth - in' sweet - er ev - er stood on feet.
Moderately slow
Gm7
C7
Gm7
C7
Gm7
D♭9+5
Ev - 'ry hon - ey bee fills with jeal - ous - y when they see you out with
mf
C11
C9
Tacet
F
F7
B♭
D♭7
Tacet
me, I don't blame them, goodness knows, hon - ey - suck - le

F
C7
F
Ab dim
Gm7
C9
rose.
When you're pass - ing by
Gm7
C9
Gm7
Db 9+5
C11
C9
Tacet
flow - ers droop and sigh,
and I know the rea - son why,
you're much sweet - er,
F
Gb maj7
G7
Ab 6
A+
Bb
C7
F
good-ness knows,
hon - ey - suck - le rose.
3
F7
Bb dim
Bdim
F7
Bb 6
F7-9
Bb dim
Bb 6
Don't buy sug - ar,
you just have to touch my cup,

G7
Cdim
C♯dim
G7
C11
you're my sug - ar, it's sweet when you
C7
Gm7
C9
Gm7
C9
stir it up. When I'm tak - in' sips from your tast - y lips,
Gm7
E♭9
D9
D♭9+5
C9
Tacet
F
F7
seems the hon - ey fair - ly drips, you're con - fec - tion, good - ness knows,
B♭
C9
F
F7
B♭
Bdim
F
C7+5
F9
hon - ey - suck - le rose.
rit.

The Joint Is Jumpin'

Words by Andy Razaf and J.C. Johnson
Music by Thomas Waller

F
C7
F
F♯dim
Gm7
C7
F7
ev - 'ry - thing is in full swing_ when you hear some - bod - y shout: (Here 'tis)
B♭
Bdim
Cm7
F7
B♭
Bdim
Cm7
F7
This joint is jump - in', it's real - ly jump - in'.
This joint is jump - in', it's real - ly jump - in'.
B♭
B♭7
E♭
Edim
B♭
F7
B♭
Come in cats_ an' check_ your hats,_ I mean_ this joint_ is jump - in'.
Ev - 'ry Mose_ is on___ his toes,_ I mean_ the joint_ is jump - in'.
D
A7
D
A7
D
A7
D
C7
The pi - an - o's thump - in', the danc - ers bump - in'.
No time for talk - in', it's time_ for walk - in'. (Yes!)

F
C7
F
F♯dim
C7
F7
This here spot_ is more than hot,_ in fact the joint is jump - in'.
Grab a jug_ and cut the rug,_ I mean this joint is jump - in'.
B♭7
Edim
B♭7
E♭
B♭7
E♭
Check your weap-ons at the door,_ be sure to pay your quar - ter.
Get your pig feet, beer and gin,_ there's plen - ty in the kitch - en.
C7
F9
C7+5
F7
Burn your leath - er on the floor,_ grab an - y - bod - y's daugh - ter.
Who is that that just came in?_ Just look at the way he's switch - in'.
B♭
Bdim
Cm7
F7
B♭
Bdim
Cm7
F7
The roof is rock - in', the neigh-bor's knock - in'.
Don't mind the hour,_ 'cause I'm in pow - er.

Bb Bb7 Eb Edim
1.
Bb F7 Bb F7
We're all bums_ when the wag-on comes._ I mean_ this joint is jump - in'. Let it beat!
I got bail_ if we go to jail._ I mean_
2.
Bb Eb Bb F+ Bb Bdim Cm7 F9 Bb Bdim
_ this joint is jump - in'. This joint is jump - in', It's real - ly jump-
Cm7 F7 Bb Bb7 Eb Ebm Bb Eb
in. We're all bums_ when the wag-on comes,_ I mean_ this joint is jump-
Bb F+ Bb Bb7 Eb Ebm Bb Bb+ Gm7 C7 F7 Bb
in'. Don't give your right name. No, No, No!

My Very Good Friend The Milkman

Words by Johnny Burke
Music by Harold Spina

Cm7 C7 Bbmaj7 C7 (C bass) Gm7 C7 D Gm
post-man says, That it would make his bur-den less If we both had the same ad-dress; And he suggests that
Gm7 C7 F NC A7 Ebm7 Ab7 Db6
you should mar-ry me.............. Then there's a ve-ry friendly fel-low who prints All the lat-est real es-tate
Dbmaj7 Db6 Ab7 Ebm7 Ab7 Db Bbm (G bass) C6 C7
news......... And ev-'ry day he sends me blue prints Of cot-tag-es with coun-try views.............. My
Fmaj7 F6 Gm7 C7 Bbmaj7 C7 (C bass)
ve-ry good friends and neighbours say, That they've been watch-ing things I do, And they be-lieve that
Gm7 C7 D Gm G7 C7 1 F Abdim Gm7 C7 2 F B9 B7 F6
I love you; So I sug-gest that you should marry me.................... My me..................
rit

Girl Of My Dreams

Words and music by Sunny Clapp

f
8

Your Feet's Too Big

Words and music by Ada Benson, Fred Fisher
and The Four Ink Spots

CHORUS to be sung after each Verse
YOUR FEET'S TOO BIG Don't want you 'cause YOUR FEET'S TOO BIG;
mf
swing tempo
F
Ab9
Cdim
C
Mad at you, 'cause YOUR FEET'S TOO BIG, Hates you 'cause YOUR FEET'S TOO
Adim
G7 Gdim G7
Dm7
D7 (5b)
F
G6
to interlude
last time
BIG.
BIG.
C Dm 7 C G7 C C#dim Dm7 G7
C F9 C
INTERLUDE
Shwa-shwa-bo, Shwa-shwa-bo, Shwa-shwa-bo, Shwa-shwa-bo,
G7 F#7 G7 F#7 G7 C B C B C
Shwa-shwa-bo, Shwa-shwa-bo, Shwa, Shwa, Shwa, Shwa-bo.
G7 F#7 G7 F#7 G7 C Cm6 C
D.S.

Handful Of Keys

Music by Thomas Waller

8va
D7
G
D7
G
F♯
8
loco
B7
E7
E7(5♭)
E7
3
A7
D7
Ddim
D7
G
Gdim
D7
Gdim
D7
G
Gdim
Cm
G
Gdim
D7

8va
f
G
Gdim
D7
G7
D7
Gdim
8
D7
G7
D7
G
Gdim
D7
8
G
Gdim
D7
G7
D7
Gdim
8
loco
8va
mp
D7
G7
D7
G
D7
G
F#
8
loco
B7
A7
B7
E7
E
A7
D7

8va
G
Gdim
D7
G7
Gdim
8
loco
D7
G7
D7
G
D7
G
f
ff
f
A♭7
G7
G11
F♯/G
G7
C
C7
F
Fm
F
C
F6
C
C7
F
Fm
C
E7
Am7
E7
A7
D7
Tacet
*

C
A7
G7
Eb
Gm
Eb
Gm
Gdim
Gm6
C7
F
Fm
C
A7
F
G11
Cdim
Am7
A7
G
F
G7
C6
D7
mf
G
Gdim
Gdim
8va
loco
D7
G
Gdim
D7

G
Gdim
D7
Gdim
D7
G
D7
G
F#
f
r.h.
l.h.
r.h.
l.h.
B7
Tacet - - - - - - - - - - - - -* A7
r.h.
r.h.
l.h.
l.h.
mf
Tacet - - - - - - - - - - - - - -* G
Gdim
D7
Gdim
D7
f
sff
Tacet - - - - - - - -* G7
Tacet - - - -* Cm
Tacet - - - - - - - - - - - -* D7
8va
G
G13

Ain't Misbehavin'

Words by Andy Razaf
Music by Thomas Waller and Harry Brooks

C Am D9 Cm6 E (B bass) F#7 B7 E G7
My love was giv - en, heart and soul,
So it can stand the test.
And made you mine a - lone for keeps,
Dit - to to all you say.
rit.
Moderately
Chorus:
C C (E bass) Dm7 G9 C C7 (G bass)
No one to talk with, all by my - self,
No one to walk with, but
mf
a tempo
F Fm C (E bass) Am7 Dm7 G9
I'm hap - py on the shelf,
Ain't Mis - be - hav - in',
I'm sav - in' my love for
E7 A7 D9 G7+5 C C (E bass)
you.
I know for cer - tain

Dm7 G9 C C7 (G bass) F Fm
the one I love, I'm thru with flirt - in', it's just you I'm think - in' of,
C (E bass) Am7 Dm7 G9 C C7 F♯dim Fm
Ain't Mis - be - hav - in', I'm sav - in' my love for you.
C (E bass) E7 Am F (A bass)
Like Jack Hor - ner in the cor - ner,
Am6 A7 G (D bass) G6 (D bass)
don't go no - where, What do I care, Your kiss - es

Am7
D9
G7
A7
D9
G7
are worth wait - in' for, be - lieve me.
C
C (E bass)
Dm7
G9
C
C7 (G bass)
I don't stay out late, don't care to go, I'm home a - bout eight, just
F
Fm
C (E bass)
Am7
Dm7
G9
me and my ra - di - o, Ain't Mis - be - hav - in', I'm sav - in' my love for
C
1.
C♯dim
Dm7
G9
2.
F7
C
you.

How Ya Baby

Words by J.C. Johnson
Music by Thomas Waller

C
(E bass)
E♭dim
Dm7
G7+5
C
Dm7
kill - er - dill - er with noth - in' on my mind.
3
E♭dim
C
Fm7
B♭9
When they start to play - in' sweet songs, it
3
E♭6
Am7
leaves me on the rocks, When they start to play - in'
D9
G7
sweet songs, it beats me to my socks. (Spoken:) How Ya

C Dm7 C F C7 F C F6 Gm F Gm
Ba - by, (Sung:) How's a - bout a lit - tle dance?
F6 Fm C (E bass) E♭dim Dm7 G9
You say you feel like truck - in', well, I'm in the groove, You
C (E bass) E♭dim Dm7 G9 C C7
feel like peck - in', come on, let's move. Ya like swing mu - sic?
A7 D9 G11 C
Yes, yes! How Ya Babe.

(What Did I Do To Be So) Black And Blue

Words by Andy Razaf
Music by Thomas Waller and Harry Brooks

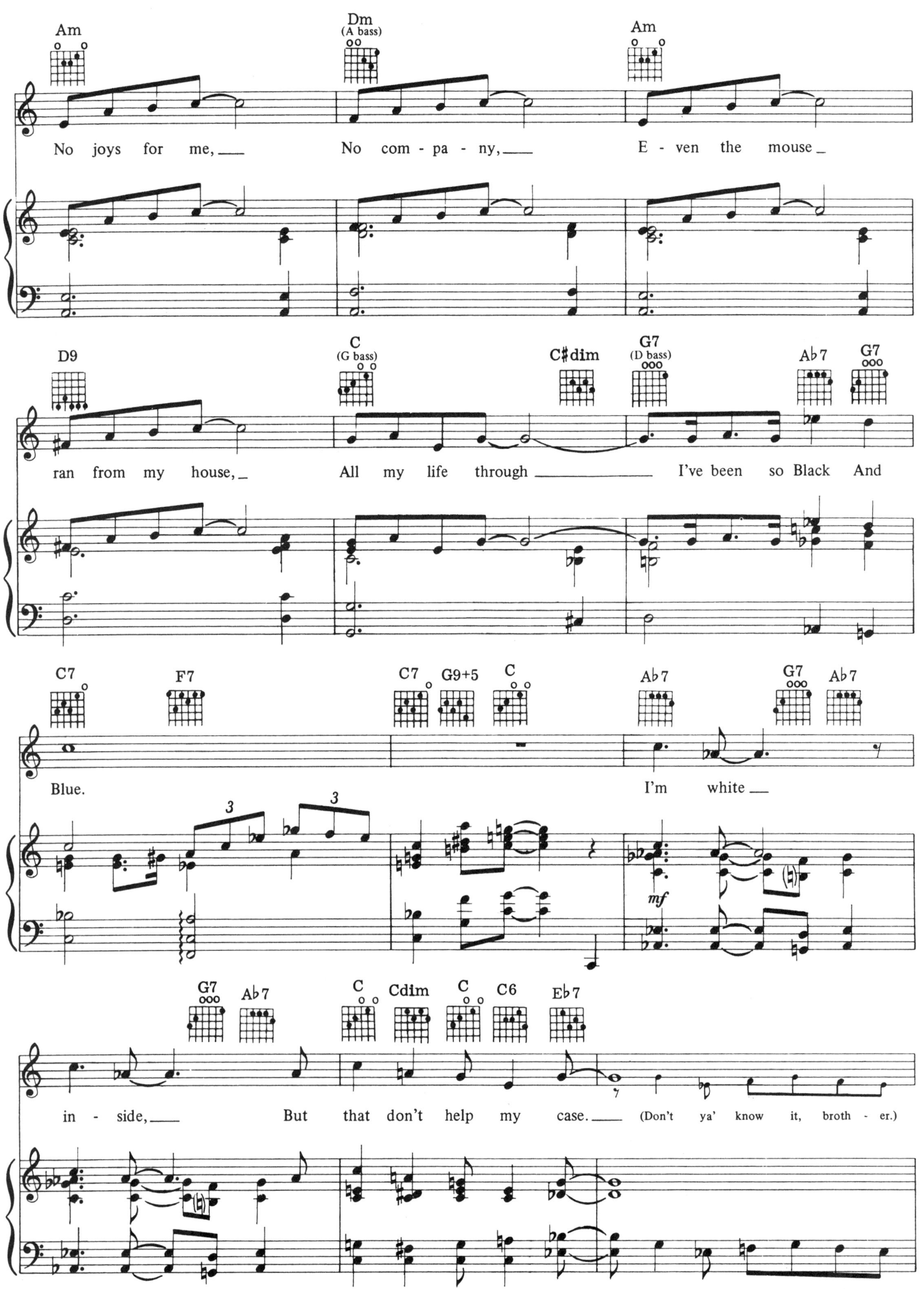
Am
Dm
(A bass)
Am
No joys for me,
No com - pa - ny,
E - ven the mouse
D9
C
(G bass)
C♯dim
G7
(D bass)
A♭7
G7
ran from my house,
All my life through
I've been so Black And
C7
F7
C7
G9+5
C
A♭7
G7
A♭7
Blue.
I'm white
mf
G7
A♭7
C
Cdim
C
C6
E♭7
in - side,
But that don't help my case.
(Don't ya' know it, broth - er.)

Ab7 G7 Ab7 G7 Ab7 Am Am (G bass) D (F# bass) F7
'Cause I can't hide what is on my
E7+5 E7 Am Dm (A bass)
face, oh! I'm so for - lorn, Life's just a thorn,
mp
Am D9 C (G bass) C#dim
My heart is torn, Why was I born? What did I do
G7 (D bass) Ab9 4 fr. G9 C F7 C
to be so Black And Blue?
ritard. e dim.

I Can't Give You Anything But Love

Words by Dorothy Fields
Music by Jimmy McHugh

D9 G7 C#dim Dm7 G7
Ba - by. Dream - in' a - while, schem - in' a - while,
C Dm7 D#dim C (E bass) A7
you're sure to find, Hap - pi - ness, an' I guess,
C (D bass) Ddim C (D bass) Ddim Am7 C (D bass) Ab7 G
all those things you've al - ways pined for. Gee, I'd like to
G (B bass) Bbdim Am7 D7 D9 G7
see you look - in' swell, Ba - by, Dia - mond brace - lets

Cmaj7
C
C
Cmaj7
Wool - worth does - n't sell, Ba - by, Till that luck - y
C♯dim
G
B7 (D♯ bass)
Bm7 (E bass)
E7
day you know darn well, Ba - by,
1.
Am7
A9
C (D bass)
D7-9
G
B♭dim
Am7
D7
I Can't Give You An - y - thing But Love.
2.
A7
D7
C (D bass)
D7-9
G6
I Can't Give You An - y - thing But Love.

'Tain't Nobody's Biz-Ness If I Do

Words and music by Porter Grainger and Everett Robbins
Additional lyric by Richard Maltby, Jr. and Murray Horwitz

Gm
B♭7
E♭7
Edim
B♭
Gm7
Cm7
F7
and I say, "Take all mine, hon - ey." 'Tain't No - bod - y's Biz - ness If I
and that leaves me in a pick - le, 'Tain't No - bod - y's Biz - ness If I
1.
D7+5
G9
C7+5
F9
Do.
2.
B♭
Cm7
C♯dim
B♭
Do.
B♭
D7
Gm
D7
There ain't noth - in' I can do nor noth - in' I can say
G7
Cm
G7
That folks don't crit - i - cize me.

*Show version

2.
Bb Cm7 C#dim Bb F#7
B D#7
Do.
If I date a real style set - ter,
If I par - ty, stay out drink - in',
G#m B7 E7 Fdim B G#m7 C#m7 F#7
4 fr.
but go home with some - one bet - ter, 'Tain't No - bod - y's Biz - ness If I
and buy me a ten - grand Lin - coln, 'Tain't No - bod - y's Biz - ness If I
1.
D#7+5 G#9 C#9+5 F#9
4 fr.
2. B C#m7 Ddim B G7
Do.
Do.
C E7 Am C7 F7 F#dim
If I feed my wife ba - lo - ney, and don't pay my al - i - mo - ny,

C
C G7 E7+5 A9 D7+5 G9 C
'Tain't No - bod - y's Biz - ness If___ I Do. If I ball_ and
E7 Am C7 F7 F♯dim C Cdim
dress up sport - y, 'n' live to die be - fore I'm for - ty, 'Tain't your biz - ness,
C Cdim C Cdim C Cdim C6 D7
'Tain't my biz - ness, 'Tain't her biz - ness, 'Tain't their biz - ness, 'Tain't No - bod - y's
cresc.
Dm7 G7-9 C F9 A♭7 C G7+5 C9
Biz - ness If___ I Do.
f

Find Out What They Like And How They Like It

Words by Andy Razaf.
Music by Thomas 'Fats' Waller.

D9
E♭7
D7
G7
Gdim
G7
C7
til I changed my plan. I'm hav - ing no more
F
C7
F
A7
Dm
trou - ble now, my dad - dy's nice as he can be.
D9
G
F7
E7
Am
Am7-5
D7
G
F
Em
G7
La - dies I will tell you how, that's if you'll take a tip from me.
poco rit.
With a "burleycue" beat
C
Cmaj9
Am7
Em7
A9
D7
G7
Find out what they like, and how they like it, and let 'em have it just that
mf

C
C♯dim
G
C
Cmaj9
Am7
Em7
A9
D7
way.
Give 'em what they want and when they want it, with - out a sin - gle word to
G7
Gdim
G7
C9
F6
say.
You've got to ca - ter to a man and if you don't he'll
Just use more sug - ar if he says your jam ain't sweet or
Now you will lose him if you give him lol - li - pops —
Now if he claims his lodge is meet - ing ev - 'ry night, it
D9
G9
C
find some oth - er gal to do the things you won't.
he will sneak for his des - sert a - cross the street.
when you know he's cra - zy just to have some chops.
means you do not han - dle all your busi - ness right.
Find out what they like, and

1.2.3.
4.
Em7 A7 D9 G7 C E♭dim Dm7 G7
how they like it, and let 'em have it just that way.
D9 G7 C A7 D9 G7
let 'em have it just that way. And let 'em have it just that
C A7 D9 G7 C C7
way. And let 'em have it just that way.
F Fm G7 C G+ C

Lookin' Good But Feelin' Bad

Words by Lester A. Santly
Music by Thomas Waller

F
C+
F
E+
E♭7
D7
lone - ly nights I'm wait - ing here for you,
G7
C7
F
Hop - in' that my love you won't re - fuse.
B♭7
A7
Dm
Am
Roh doh doh doh doh doh doh.
Dm
Am
Dm
Roh doh doh doh doh.
Roh doh doh doh

Bb7
No chord
G9
C7
doh doh doh. Bah bah bah bah bah bah.
F
C+
F
C+
F
E+
Eb7
Look - in' Good But Feel - in' Bad is might - y hard to
D7
G7
C7
do, When I'm feel - in' blue and need - ing you.
F
Db7
C7
F6
(And need - ing you.)